Boom Boom

Popular Movie and TV Songs

For Boomwhackers® Musical Tubes

- **10 Great Movie and TV Songs**
- **Cool CD With Full Performance and Accompaniment Tracks**
- **Includes Teaching Suggestions and Reproducible Visuals**
- **Kid-Tested!**

This is a joint publication between Warner Bros. Publications and Whacky Music, Inc.

BOOMWHACKERS® Tuned Percussion Tubes are a product of Whacky Music, Inc., of Sedona, Arizona.

"BOOMWHACKERS" is a registered trademark licensed to Whacky Music, Inc. Visit the Whacky Music Web site at *www.boomwhackers.com.*

Special thanks to our wonderful field-testers,
the sixth-grade music classes from Good Shepherd Episcopal School in Dallas, Texas, and
their teacher/director, Chris Judah-Lauder.

Arranger/Editor: Gayle Giese
Consultant: Chris Judah-Lauder
Recording Producer: Teena Chinn
Art Cover Design: Thais Yanes
Music Engraving and Text Layout: Adrian Alvarez
Text Editor: Nadine DeMarco
Production Coordinator: Sharon Marlow

General Teaching Suggestions

Although teaching suggestions are provided for each song, here are some general tips to help you and your students thoroughly enjoy playing the ten fun movie and TV songs in this book.

Use the cool CD that is included! Before teaching the Boomwhacker® parts for a particular song, play the full performance version on the CD so that students will get the song in their ears. After students are familiar with the song, assign parts and distribute the Boomwhackers®.

Sometimes, reproducible teaching visuals are provided when our field-test group indicated that they were needed. Feel free to copy and enlarge the visuals. The musical notes used on the visuals have open note heads so that you can color them in with colors that match the Boomwhacker® tubes.

Once students have the skills to play through the entire song, they will enjoy playing and performing with the accompaniment tracks on the CD. Occasionally, you'll hear some melody notes even on the accompaniment tracks to reinforce the tune when the Boomwhacker® melody part may be difficult for some players. Of course, students may also play along with the full performance tracks. Clicks sound at the start of each track to set the tempo and allow students to prepare to play.

Occasionally, tremolos or rolls or even repeated pitches appear because the tubes make a staccato rather than a sustaining sound. Practice the tremolos (some teachers may prefer to call these "rolls") by having students hold an empty hand close to the floor, thigh, or other playing surface and quickly bounce the tube back and forth between the surface and the hand (fingers or palm). Another way is to sit on the floor with feet about five inches apart and bounce the tube back and forth between the shoe soles. Tennis shoes work great! If the student is standing with feet shoulder-width apart, the tubes can be bounced between knees. Experiment!

Octavator™ caps are available for Boomwhacker® tubes, and they are super! These caps easily attach to either end of the tube and lower the tube's pitch by an octave, creating a very resonant sound. When using the caps, students can hold the tube perpendicular to the floor and gently bounce the capped end of the tube on the floor. The sound is best on a lightly carpeted surface; strips of felt can be placed on a hard surface. Use the caps or the bass tubes whenever you see 8vb below the notes in arrangements within this book. (In the "Required Tubes" section, these are listed as "Low" pitches.) Many arrangements suggest 8vb throughout the accompaniment part so that it sounds in the range of most left-hand piano parts. There are a few optional uses of 15mb (down two octaves); this requires the use of a bass tube with an Octavator™ cap.

All ten songs in this book require the use of at least one set of the eight C Major Diatonic Scale tubes and one set of the Bass Diatonic set of seven tubes. Another option (preferred by the editor) is to use two C Major Diatonic sets and place Octavator™ caps on one set. Additional sets provide more teaching flexibility, allowing students to hold a tube in each hand or to have several students play tubes of the same pitch. For some songs, you may want to strengthen the melody by having more melody players than accompaniment players. Of the ten movie and TV songs in this book, four songs also require the use of chromatics tubes. This is indicated in the "Required Tubes" section for each song.

Arrangements were written for upper elementary and middle school general music classes, offering both melody and accompaniment parts. You may teach all parts or only one part or section and play it along with the CD. Feel free to adapt the arrangements depending on the skill and number of students in your classes. All parts in the visuals and the score are shown in treble clef. With only slight adjustment, some of these arrangements can also be played on Orff barred instruments as indicated in the teaching suggestions for each song.

Finally, have fun! These are familiar songs that students will be eager to play—and now they can play them on the fun Boomwhacker® musical tubes.

—the Editor

CONTENTS

Editor's Note

This songbook is one of a series of materials for Boomwhackers® Musical Tubes being jointly developed by Warner Bros. Publications and Whacky Music, Inc., which manufactures Boomwhackers®. Whacky Music recognizes the important value these materials add to its unique musical tubes and is proud to have the opportunity to cooperate with Warner Bros. Publications in their development.

The color-coded, plastic Boomwhackers® tubes were invented by Craig Ramsell, president of Whacky Music, after being inspired by a cardboard gift-wrap tube that he had cut in two in preparation for recycling. As of this writing in 2001, more than one million Boomwhackers® have been shipped into the world. Because they are fun, easy to play, and inexpensive, a large number of them are being used in thousands of schools around the world for music education. They have received numerous awards, including a Parents' Choice Gold Award, Dr. Toy's Best 100 Children's Products, and an Oppenheim Toy Portfolio Gold Seal.

Jeopardy Theme

Tubes required:

(Tubes are listed in order of occurrence in the music for each part. For the "Low" tubes, use bass tubes or tubes with Octavator™ caps.)

Melody: C   F   Low F   A   G   D   Low B♭   Low A   Low G

Accompaniment: Low F   Low C   Low D   Low E
Optional: Very Low F (two octaves below F'; use a bass tube with an Octavator™ cap)

Teaching suggestions:

- Give each student one or two tubes as shown below. Seat all but four students in a semicircle:
  Low F / C & F / A & G / F & D / D & C / Low B♭ & Low A / Low F / Low G / Low A
- Seat the four remaining students in front and middle to play the accompaniment:
  Low F / Low C & Low D / Low E & Low F / Very Low F (opt.)

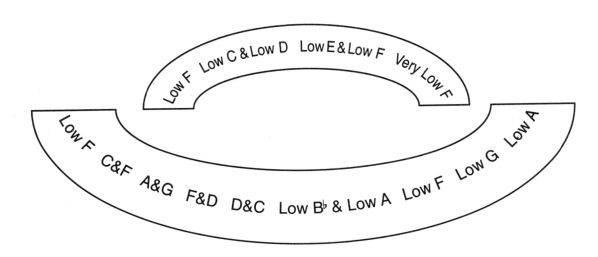

- Teach parts by rote.
- The melody also works well on Orff barred instruments.

Jeopardy Theme

Music by
MERV GRIFFIN

Thoughtfully

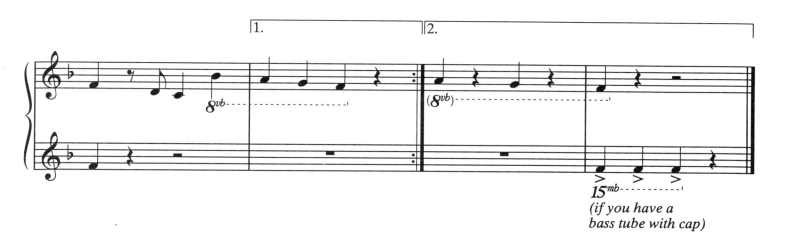

Star Wars
(Main Theme)

Tubes required:

(Tubes are listed in order of occurrence in the music for each part. For the "Low" tubes, use bass tubes or tubes with Octavator™ caps.)

Melody:

A Section:	Low G	C	G	F	D	High C	E	
B Section:	Low A	F	E	D	C	Low B	Low G	G	High C

Accompaniment (chords):

A Section --

> **Pattern 1:** Low E, Low G   Low C, Low B
> **Pattern 2:** Low F, Low A   ,Low C, Low E
> **Pattern 3:** Low F, Low A   Low G, Low B

B Section --

> **Pattern 4:** Low F, Low G
> **Pattern 5:** Low G, Low B
> **Pattern 6:** Low D, Low F   Low F, Low G

Teaching suggestions:

- Seat the accompaniment players together who play the same pattern, giving the same player both tubes that occur in a chord. Note that Pattern 6 occurs only once; swap parts so students can have more chances to play.
- Teach the accompaniment patterns first and use the form visual to put the patterns together in the correct order for performance.
- In field-testing, it was discovered that the melody is very difficult to teach by rote. Use the melody visual and color the notes to match the tubes and teach the melody.
- You could use the melody visual to review music notation skills, asking students to color in their notes and name the pitches.
- Both the melody and accompaniment would work well on Orff barred instruments if players are competent.
- You could do just the **A** section if the entire piece is too long for your group. May the force be with you!

Star Wars
(Main Theme)

By JOHN WILLIAMS

Melody Visual

Star Wars
(Main Theme)

Copy, enlarge, and color in the noteheads to match the tubes.

By JOHN WILLIAMS

Form Visual

Star Wars
(Main Theme)

Copy and enlarge.

Accompaniment Patterns
Suggested Form:

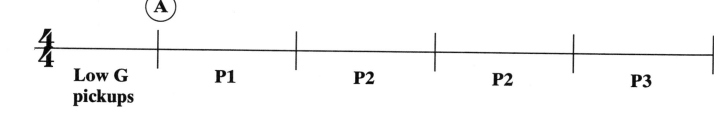

$\mathbf{A}$

$\begin{array}{c} 4 \\ 4 \end{array}$ | **Low G pickups** | **P1** | **P2** | **P2** | **P3** |

(A) | **P1** | **P2** | **P2** | **P3** |

(B) | **P4** | **P4** | **P4** | **P5** |

(B) | **P4** | **P4** | **P6** | **P5** |

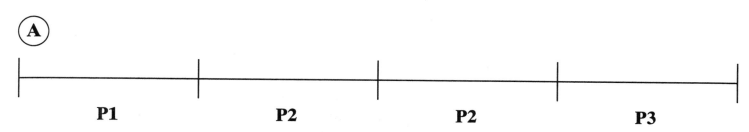

(A) | **P1** | **P2** | **P2** | **P3** |

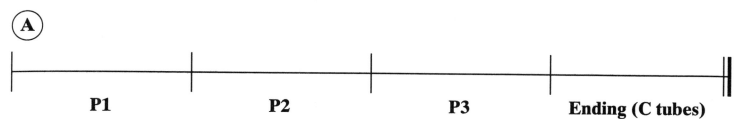

(A) | **P1** | **P2** | **P3** | **Ending (C tubes)** |

Gonna Fly Now
(Theme from "Rocky")

Tubes required:

(Tubes are listed in order of occurrence in the music for each part. For the "Low" tubes, use bass tubes or tubes with Octavator™ caps.)

Introduction: E (played with Accompaniment Pattern 6)

Accompaniment Patterns (chords):
Pattern 1: Low E, Low F, Low A, C
Pattern 2: Low C, Low E, Low G, Low B
Pattern 3: Low D, Low F, Low A
Pattern 4: Low E, Low G, Low B
Pattern 5: Low F, C
Pattern 6: Low D, Low E, Low B
Pattern 7: Low C, Low E, Low A

Teaching suggestions:

Accompaniment:
- Seat students on the floor with their pattern partners. Organize groups around the room in the order of the seven patterns.
- Teach the seven different patterns first. Practice by having students pat the steady beat as their patterns occur and then transfer the patting to the playing of the tubes.
- Then use the visual to play the patterns in order.
- The accompaniment also works well on Orff barred instruments.

Melody:
You or a talented student could play the melody on recorder or Orff keyboard instruments. The melody is played on recorder on the full performance and accompaniment tracks.

Introduction:
- Give each child two E tubes, one for each hand. Provide a speech rhyme such as:
  I wanna go wanna (ʔ) va-room / go wanna go boom boom!
- Once students can confidently and repeatedly speak these words in the correct rhythm, play the rhythm on Boomwhacker® tubes. Add Accompaniment Pattern 6, patting it first to establish the steady beat.

Gonna Fly Now
(Theme from "Rocky")

By BILL CONTI, AYN ROBBINS
and CAROL CONNORS

Intro:

Melody

(Pattern 6)
8vb *throughout* ⟶

Play melody on recorder or Orff instruments;
simplify rhythms if needed. Melody also occurs on both CD tracks.

(Pattern 1)
Accompaniment   *(P2)*   *(P1)*   *(P2)*

(P3)   *(P4)*   *(P5)*   *(P5)*

1.   2.

Fade

(P6)   *(P6)*   *(P6)*   *(P7)*   *(P6)*

* may omit eighth notes in accompaniment.

12

Visual

Gonna Fly Now
(Theme from "Rocky")

Copy and enlarge.

Accompaniment Patterns

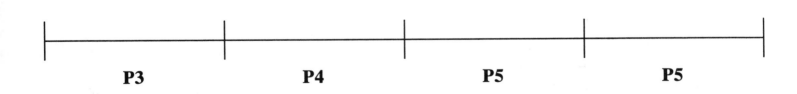

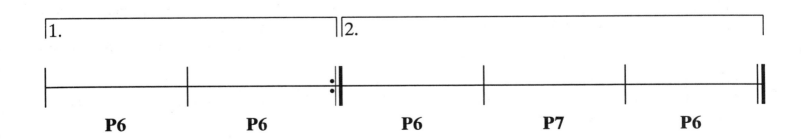

The Ballad of Gilligan's Isle

Tubes required:

(Tubes are listed in order of occurrence in the music for each part. For the "Low" tubes, use bass tubes or tubes with Octavator™ caps.)

Melody: E   Low A   D   Low B   Low G   G   C   B   A

Accompaniment: Low A   Low G

Teaching suggestions:

- Give each student one or two tubes. Students who play the tremolo notes (E, G, D, Low G) should hold two tubes of the same pitch (if available) in each hand. Note that B and A only play at the end of the melody part and that the entire accompaniment part is played on Low A and Low G.
- Seat the melody players in a large semicircle, with the accompaniment players in a smaller semicircle in front and in the middle of the others.
- The accompaniment also works well on Orff barred instruments.

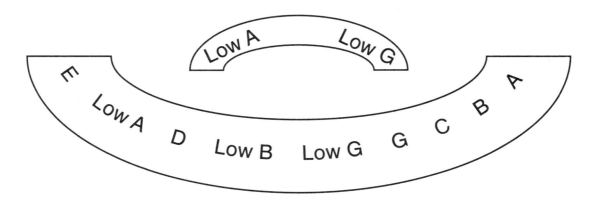

- Use the visual to copy and color the notes to match the tubes to teach the melody.
- Omit the pickup note (E) if it's too difficult for your students.
- To sustain the sound of the longer melody notes, have students practice playing tremolos or rolls. See the General Teaching Suggestions on page 2 for optional ways to play tremolos.
- Once students can play the melody for verses 1 - 3, have them sing along with the entire song, following the words in the visual.
- Playing the melody (top line) for verse 4 may be too difficult. If so, enjoy singing the verse to end Gilligan's story and accompany with only the Low A and Low G tubes as shown in the music.
- To make the accompaniment easier to teach by rote, we've kept the rhythm pattern the same except in the last three measures.
- Allow players to swap parts.
- Consider having some students act out the parts of Gilligan, the skipper, the millionaire and his wife, the movie star, and the rest (the professor and Mary Ann).

The Ballad of Gilligan's Isle

Words and Music by
SHERWOOD SCHWARTZ and GEORGE WYLE

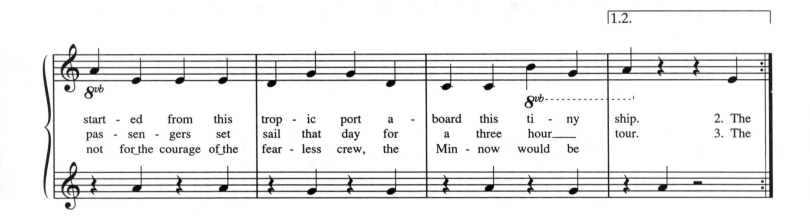

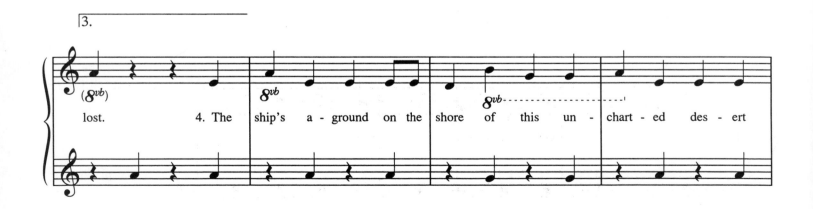

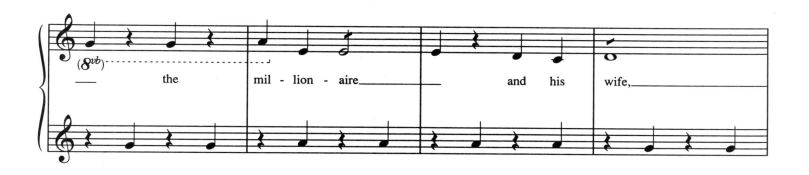

Visual

The Ballad of Gilligan's Isle

Copy, enlarge, and color in the noteheads to match the tubes.

Words and Music by
SHERWOOD SCHWARTZ and GEORGE WYLE

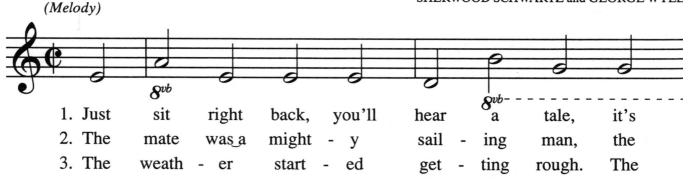

1. Just sit right back, you'll hear a tale, it's
2. The mate was a might - y sail - ing man, the
3. The weath - er start - ed get - ting rough. The

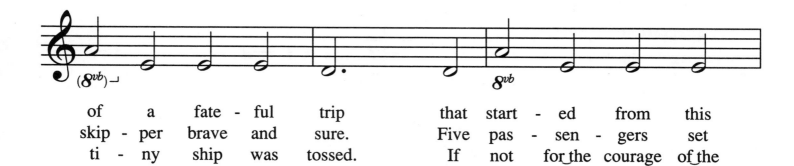

of a fate - ful trip that start - ed from this
skip - per brave and sure. Five pas - sen - gers set
ti - ny ship was tossed. If not for the courage of the

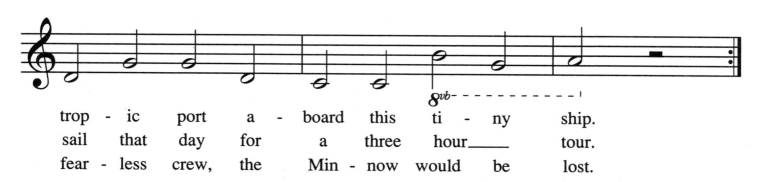

trop - ic port a - board this ti - ny ship.
sail that day for a three hour tour.
fear - less crew, the Min - now would be lost.

Verse 4:
The ship's aground on the shore
Of this uncharted desert isle,
With Gilligan, the skipper too,
The millionaire and his wife,
The movie star and the rest
Are here on Gilligan's Isle!

Once Upon a December

Tubes required:

(Tubes are listed in order of occurrence in the music for each part. For the "Low" tubes, use bass tubes or tubes with Octavator™ caps.)

Pattern 1: Low A   Low E (Pattern 1 players also play on optional ending chord.)
Pattern 2: Low B   Low E (and one High C in the Coda)
Pattern 3: Low D   Low F   Low A
Pattern 4: Low E   Low D

Optional Melody: E   F   G   D   C   Low A   Low B   A   B
High C, A, E (opt. last chord)

Teaching suggestions:

- Seat students with their pattern partners and in the order of the patterns they play.
- Use the visual to learn the accompaniment patterns and put them in order to play along with the full performance or accompaniment CD tracks. The full performance track uses Boomwhacker® tubes for the melody, while the accompaniment track uses other instruments.
- Low A, Low E, and C tubes will play tremolos in the Coda section. See the General Teaching Suggestions on page 2 for optional ways to play tremolos.
- The accompaniment would also work well on Orff barred instruments.
- Learn the words and sing the beautiful melody. Is it major or minor?
- The melody is very difficult to play on Boomwhackers®. If you try it, have the D, E, Low A, Low B, C, and A players practice the tremolos (rolls).
- If possible, assign more melody than accompaniment players (if you try the melody).
- Another option is to play the melody on Orff barred instruments.
- If you feel that the piece is too long, an option is to go straight to the Coda the first time through.

Once Upon a December

Music by STEPHEN FLAHERTY
Lyrics by LYNN AHRENS

Visual

Once Upon a December

Copy, enlarge, and color in the noteheads to match the tubes.

Accompaniment Patterns

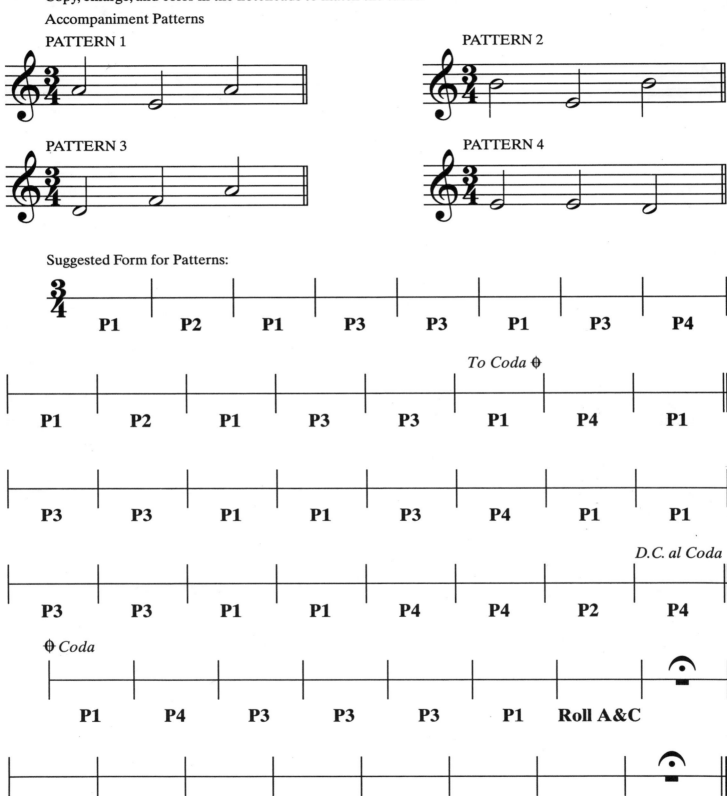

Batman Theme
(From the TV Series)

Tubes required:

(Tubes are listed in order of occurrence in the music for each part. For the "Low" tubes, use bass tubes or tubes with Octavator™ caps.)

Pattern A (top and bottom staffs): Low G (throughout pattern)   D   C♯   C♮
(Seat three students together to play D, C♯, and C; if you have enough tubes, give each student two each of the same pitch. Seat one student facing them to play two Low G tubes.)

Melody 1: F, G
(Assign two students to play Melody 1 with each holding one F and one G tube.)

Pattern B (top and bottom staffs): Low C (throughout pattern)   Low G   Low F♯   Low F♮
(Seat three students together to play Low G, Low F♯, and Low F; seat one student facing them to play two Low C tubes.)

Melody 2: B♭, High C
(Assign two students to play Melody 2 with each holding one B♭ and one High C tube.)

Pattern C (top and bottom staffs): Low D (throughout pattern)   A   A♭   G
(Seat three students together to play A, A♭, and G; seat one student facing them to play two Low D tubes.)

Melody 3: C, D

Optional Ending (all three staffs): D, Low G (from Pattern A)
Low D, Low G, F, G, B♭ (final two chords; anyone with these tubes should play!)

Teaching suggestions:

- See seating and tube assignment suggestions above. There are three basic harmonies (patterns), all with straight eighth-note rhythms. Learn these one at a time, adding the melody line that goes with it before moving on to the next pattern.
- Copy and enlarge the visual to help put the sections together for performance. The letters represent the patterns, and the numbers represent the melodic parts. The form is only a suggestion; feel free to adapt it to your needs.
- Younger children will enjoy moving to the "bat" music. If possible, invite some younger classes in to hear your Boomwhacker® ensemble play "Batman Theme."

Batman Theme
(From the TV Series)

Words and Music by
NEAL HEFTI

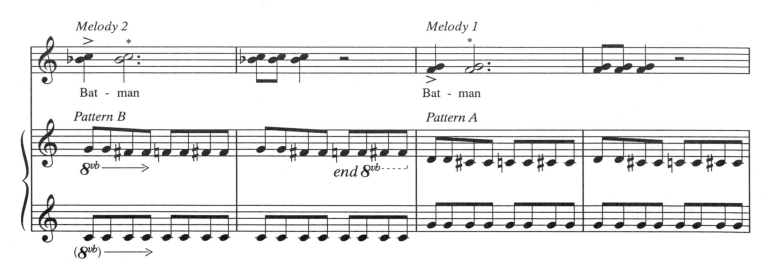

* Optional tremolo roll: older students may hold two tubes of different pitches such as F & G and alternate playing them rapidly on the floor.

† Have students play their Boomwhackers® as quickly as they can, like a drum roll.

Batman Theme - 2 - 2

Visual

Batman Theme
(From the TV Series)

Copy and enlarge.

Suggested Final Form: Letters = Accompaniment Patterns
Numbers = Melody

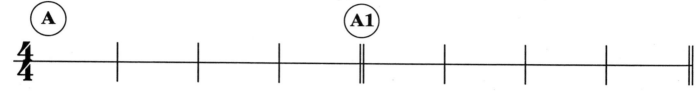

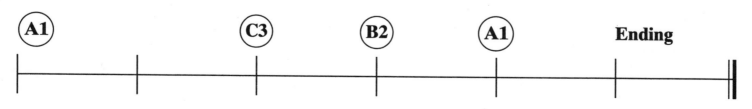

Over the Rainbow

Tubes required:

(Tubes are listed in order of occurrence in the music for each part. For the "Low" tubes, use bass tubes or tubes with Octavator™ caps.)

Intro (top line):   E   G   F   A   D
(The ending also requires B and High C, or these notes could just be sung.)

Intro (bottom line):   C   Low B   Low A   Low G   Low F
(The ending also requires Low E.)

Accompaniment:
   Pattern 1: Low E   Low G
   Pattern 2: Low F   Low A
   Pattern 3: Low C   Low E
   Pattern 4: Low F   Low G
   Pattern 5: Low G   Low F   Low E   Low D
   Pattern 6: A (Pattern 6 occurs only once; assign to one student and trade parts.)

Teaching suggestions:

• Boomwhacker® tubes play the top and bottom lines of the introduction and the last seven measures of the piece, including the pickup to that ending section. Boomwhacker® tubes also play the accompaniment patterns throughout the song.
• Distribute tubes and seat students according to the patterns they will play. There are six patterns plus the four-measure introduction that recurs (see music). Note that the top line of the introduction uses Patterns 1, 4, 6, and 5, but up an octave.
• Use the visual, color-coding the notes to teach the four-bar introduction.
• Teach the seven patterns by rote. Practice playing straight eighth notes, first patting laps and then transferring to the tubes.
• Add the Ending, using the visual. Note that it begins exactly like the introduction, using the same first four measures, followed by the final three measures shown on the visual. Everyone with C, E, or G tubes plays a tremolo (roll) on the last chord. See the General Teaching Suggestions on page 2 for optional ways to play tremolos. Have students practice playing the tremolos until you cut off the music with a hand motion. This could lead to a discussion of the fermata.
• The beautiful melody, which needs to be legato, with sustained tones, could be sung or played on keyboard or wind instruments or a combination of these.
• Use the visual when you are ready to put all the parts together and perform the piece.
• The accompaniment would also work well on Orff barred instruments.

Over the Rainbow

Music by HAROLD ARLEN
Words by E.Y. HARBURG

Intro: Play on Boomwhackers®

8vb thoughout ⟶

A Melody (Voices or keyboard or Orff instruments)

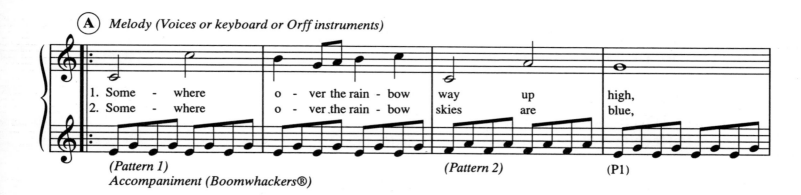

1. Some - where o - ver the rain - bow way up high,
2. Some - where o - ver the rain - bow skies are blue,

(Pattern 1)
Accompaniment (Boomwhackers®)
(Pattern 2) (P1)

1.

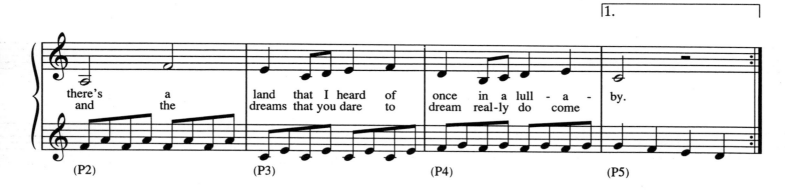

there's a
and the
land that I heard of
dreams that you dare to
once in a lull - a -
dream real-ly do come
by.

(P2) (P3) (P4) (P5)

2. **B**

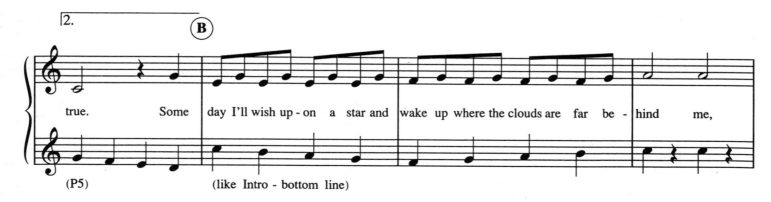

true. Some day I'll wish up-on a star and wake up where the clouds are far be - hind me,

(P5) (like Intro - bottom line)

Visual

Over the Rainbow

Copy, enlarge, and color in the noteheads to match the tubes.

Music by HAROLD ARLEN
Words by E.Y. HARBURG

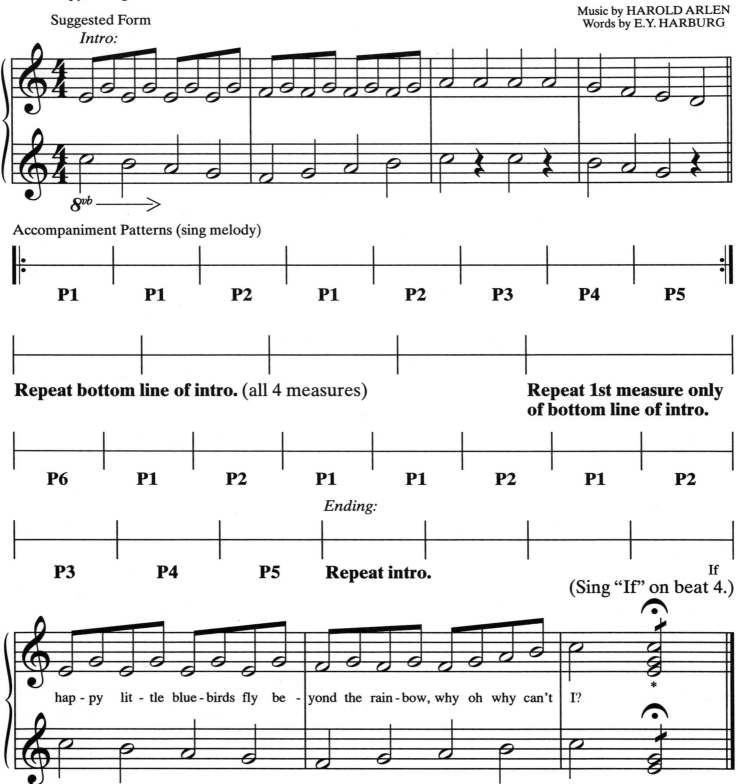

* All C, E, and G tubes roll.

The Lion Sleeps Tonight

Key of F

Key of G

Tubes required:

(Tubes are listed in order of occurrence in the music for each part. For the "Low" tubes, use bass tubes or tubes with Octavator™ caps.)

Part 1 (Melody):   Low F   Low G   Low A   Low B♭   C

Part 2 (four eighth-note chord patterns):   C, F   Low B♭, D   Low A, C   Low B♭, C

Combine Parts 1 and 2 to create Part 3. (See music; Part 2 repeats.)

Teaching suggestions:

- Seat Part 1 and Part 2 players in separate sections. They could face each other on two sides of the room.

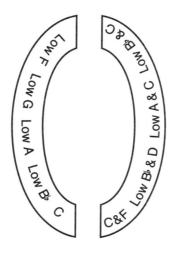

- For Part 2, divide students into four groups—one group for each measure; position these students in the order that their notes are played.
- Teach Part 2 first.
- Use the visual to teach Part 1 (melody). Copy and enlarge and color the notes to match the tubes.
- Have students playing the Low G tubes practice the tremolos (or rolls) on the whole and dotted half notes in Part 1. See the General Teaching Suggestions on page 2 for optional ways to play tremolos.
- Combine Parts 1 and 2 to create Part 3, playing Part 2 twice. End on an F chord. Have fun!

- Try the version in the key of G, assigning a student to play Part 1 (melody) on the recorder or an Orff barred instrument. The CD includes full performance and accompaniment tracks for Key of F and Key of G versions.

The Lion Sleeps Tonight

Key of F version
(Also see Key of G version
with Recorder/Orff instrument part.)

Lyrics and Revised Music by
GEORGE DAVID WEISS,
HUGO PERETTI and LUIGI CREATORE

Part 1 (Melody)

In the jun - gle, the might - y jun - gle, the li - on sleeps to - night.

In the jun - gle, the qui - et jun - gle, the li - on sleeps to - night.

Part 2

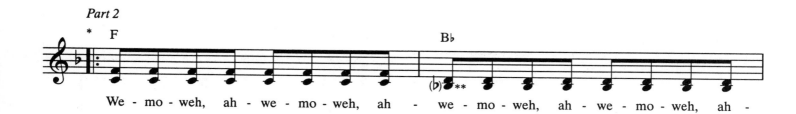

We - mo - weh, ah - we - mo - weh, ah - we - mo - weh, ah - we - mo - weh, ah -

we - mo - weh, ah - we - mo - weh, ah - we - mo - weh, ah - we - mo - weh, ah -

Part 3: Combine Parts 1 and 2 playing Part 2 twice! End with everyone playing notes in an F chord. Have fun!

* Straight rhythms are written for ease of learning, but you may want to swing them! ♫=♪♪
** Use caps or bass tubes for notes below middle C.

The Lion Sleeps Tonight

Key of G version

Play Part 1 (Melody) on recorder or Orff barred instrument.

Lyrics and Revised Music by
GEORGE DAVID WEISS,
HUGO PERETTI and LUIGI CREATORE

Part 1 (Melody)

Part 2

We - mo - weh, ah - we - mo - weh, ah - we - mo - weh, ah - we - mo - weh, ah -

we - mo - weh, ah - we - mo - weh, ah - we - mo - weh, ah - we - mo - weh, ah -

Part 3: Combine Parts 1 and 2 playing Part 2 twice! End with everyone playing notes in a G chord. Have fun!

* Straight rhythms are written for ease of learning, but you may want to swing them!

** Use caps or bass tubes for this B:

Visual

The Lion Sleeps Tonight

Copy, enlarge, and color in the noteheads to match the tubes.

Lyrics and Revised Music by
GEORGE DAVID WEISS,
HUGO PERETTI and LUIGI CREATORE

The Pink Panther

Tubes required:

(Tubes are listed in order of occurrence in the music for each part. For the "Low" tubes, use bass tubes or tubes with Octavator™ caps.)

Optional Intro top line and Optional Melody: Low F♯ Low G Low G♯   Low A   Low B
C   F   E   E♭   D   A   A♭   G

Intro bottom line: Low F♯   Low G   Low G♯   Low A   Low C♯   Low D   Low D♯   Low E

Accompaniment:
   Pattern 1: Low E   Low A
   Pattern 2: Low F   Low C
   Pattern 3: Low B♭   Low F

Coda top line: Low A   A   G   E   D   C   E♭   Low G   E, G♯, B (final chord)

Optional Coda bottom line: Low E   Low A   Low G   Low D   Low C   Low A♭
Low F♯   Low F   Very Low A (opt.; use a bass tube with an Octavator™ cap)   Low A, C (final chord)

Teaching suggestions:

- If you decide to play all melody and accompaniment parts on "The Pink Panther," you'll need a minimum of 40 students! So, we put the melody on both CD tracks (with Boomwhacker® tubes playing the melody on the full performance version) so you could just teach the accompaniment patterns, coda, and optional introduction and play along with the CD.
- Listen to the CD tracks and have the children pat or snap along.
- Teach the three accompaniment patterns by rote, or use the visual and color the notes to match the tubes.
- Discuss and explain the signs in the music that make up the musical roadmap: *To Coda* ⊕, *D.S.* 𝄋 *al Coda,* and ⊕ *Coda.*
- Teach the bottom line of the introduction by rote; advanced groups could add the top line.
- See the General Teaching Suggestions on page 2 for optional ways to play tremolos in the introduction, melody line, and coda.
- Use the visual and color the notes to match the tubes to teach the Coda.
- Use the visual to put the whole piece together for performance.
- Invite younger students to a performance, and have them dance on tiptoes to the music.

The Pink Panther

By HENRY MANCINI

Mysteriously; in 2

* 𝅗𝅥. = tremolo or roll.

* Keep playing chord until teacher/director cuts off. It's cool!

Visual

The Pink Panther

Copy, enlarge, and color in the noteheads to match the tubes.

Accompaniment Patterns

By HENRY MANCINI

Singin' in the Rain

Tubes required:

(Tubes are listed in order of occurrence in the music for each part. For the "Low" tubes, use bass tubes or tubes with Octavator™ caps.)

Melody: C   High C   A   G   F   D   E

Accompaniment:

Pattern 1: Low F   Low A   Low C

Pattern 2: Low G   C   Low E

Pattern 3: Low C   Low D   Low E

Teaching suggestions:

- Teach (by rote) the three accompaniment patterns first. Seat these players in three separate groups, according to the pattern they will play. Use four to six players for each pattern. For example, on Pattern 1, two students might each play Low F and Low A while two others might play only the Low C. Pattern 3 players don't get to play as much as the other two groups, so swap parts after awhile. The patterns would also work well on bass xylophone.
- Use the form visual to teach the order in which patterns occur.
- Consider playing the melody on recorder.
- Seat Boomwhacker® melody players together and use the melody visual, coloring the notes to match the tubes. Point to the notes as the students play them.
- Practice the tremolos, which occur on High C, D, and F; assign the most coordinated and rhythmical students to play these melody notes. See the General Teaching Suggestions on page 2 for optional ways to play tremolos (rolls). It's not important to roll four exact eighth notes as long as rolls end together.
- The next-to-last measure is optional and could be omitted, or you could continue *Accompaniment Pattern 1* without the melody part.
- Practice the last measure separately with the F and Low F tubes playing together on beats 1 and 3.

Singin' in the Rain

Music by NACIO HERB BROWN
Lyric by ARTHUR FREED

Melody

3

(Pattern 1)
Accompaniment
8vb throughout ⟶

I'm sing - in' in the rain, just

sing - in' in the rain. What a glo - ri - ous feel - ing, I'm

11

hap - py a - gain. I'm laugh - ing at clouds so

(Pattern 2)

dark up a - bove, the sun's___ in my heart___ and I'm

(Pattern 3)

* ♩ = tremolo or roll.

Singin' in the Rain - 2 - 1

* This measure may be omitted or continue Accompaniment Pattern 1 only.

Melody Visual

Singin' in the Rain

Music by NACIO HERB BROWN
Lyric by ARTHUR FREED

Copy, enlarge, and color in the noteheads to match the tubes.

I'm sing - in' in the

rain, just sing - in' in the rain. What a

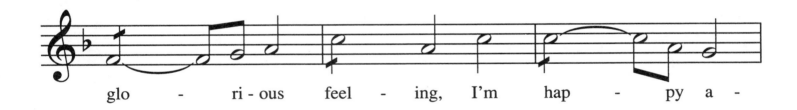

glo - ri - ous feel - ing, I'm hap - py a -

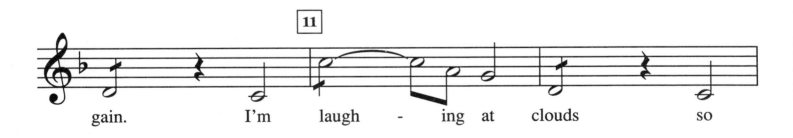

gain. I'm laugh - ing at clouds so

dark up a - bove, the sun's_____ in my

Singin' in the Rain - 2 - 1

(Melody Visual p. 2)

* This measure may be omitted or continue Accompaniment Pattern 1 only.

Form Visual

Singin' in the Rain

Copy and enlarge.

Accompaniment Patterns

Suggested Form:

|3|

$\frac{4}{4}$ P1   P1   P1   P1   P1

P1   P1   P1   P2   P2

|11|

P2   P2   P2   P2   P2

|19|

P3   P1   P3   P1   P1

P1   P3   P1   P1   P2

|27|

P2   P2   P2   P2   P2

|34|

P2   P2   P1   P1   **Optional Ending:**
Play F on beats 1 & 3
or roll all F, A, C tubes.

Bowmar's
ADVENTURES
IN MUSIC LISTENING
An Integrated Elementary Listening Program
for Kindergarten through 8th Grade Classes

By Dr. Leon Burton, Dr. Charles Hoffer, Dr. William Hughes and June Hinckley

- A fun, innovative approach to music listening for today's student
- Directly correlated with the National Standards in Music Education Goals 2000
- Easy-to-follow lesson plan format
- Active participation experiences for students in every lesson

Includes great works by:
Bizet, Debussy, Ravel, Tchaikovsky, Bach, Mozart, Verdi, Grieg
and many others

Level 1, Grades K-2

The Teacher's Guide/CD — Level 1 (BMR08201)
contains lesson plans for each of the 32 musical selections, including:

- Anticipated Outcomes
- Historical Information
- Composer Information
- Musical Features Sketch
- Cross-Curricular Connections
- National Standards
- Full-length CD

The Big Book — Level 1 (BMR08201B)
contains magnificent full-color illustrations depicting each of the 32 pieces in the program

Student Activity Book — Level 1 (BMR08201S)
provides individual and group experiences that reinforce the learning in each lesson

Student Coloring Book — Level 1 (BMR08201C)
contains the Big Book illustrations re-created and ready for students' coloring activity (with our permission to photocopy)

Selected pages from
Big Book, Level 1

Level 2, Grades 3-5

The Teacher's Guide/CD — Level 2 (BMR08202)
contains lesson plans for each of the 20 musical selections, including:

- Anticipated Outcomes
- Historical Information
- Composer Information
- Musical Features Sketch
- Cross-Curricular Connections
- National Standards
- Full-length CD

Student Activity Book — Level 2 (BMR08202S)
provides individual and group experiences that reinforce the learning in each lesson

Level 3, Grades 6-8

The Teacher's Guide/CD — Level 3 (BMR08203)
contains lesson plans for each of the 25 musical selections, including:

- Anticipated Outcomes
- Historical Information
- Composer Information
- Musical Features Sketch
- Cross-Curricular Connections
- National Standards
- Full-length CD

Student Activity Book — Level 3 (BMR08203S)
provides individual and group experiences that reinforce the learning in each lesson

We Salute the
National Music Standards

WARNER BROS. PUBLICATIONS
A Warner Music Group Company

Available at your local music store

WB DANCE SERIES is ideal for school music programs, P.E. classes, dance classes, camp programs, or after-school fun!

Kids love to dance! WB Dance Series is sure to create dance fever, and it's contagious! Greg Gilpin has designed WB DANCE SERIES especially for kids ages 6-10. The moves are easy and exciting, and the songs are fun for children to sing. Greg is an experienced choreographer and clinician and is recognized as a leader in the show choir movement.

Each set includes two dance tunes with lyrics, choreography, and a super-pro CD with complete performance and separate accompaniment tracks.

Set 1 (BMR07011CD):
(We're Gonna)
Rock Around the Clock
Peppermint Twist

Set 2 (0556B):
Shake Rattle and Roll
Happy Feet!

Set 3 (0557B):
Fame
Charleston

Set 4 (0620B):
We're Off to See the Wizard
Ease On Down the Road

Set 5 (BMR07014CD):
Old Time Rock & Roll
Do Wah Diddy Diddy

Set 6 (BMR07015CD):
Love Potion No. 9
Yellow Bird

AD508A 10/01 Printed in USA